Problems With

Pete the Pencil
and
Eddie the Eraser

Scholastic Inc.
New York · Toronto · London · Auckland · Sydney · Mexico City · New Delhi · Hong Kong · Buenos Aires

We would like
to dedicate
this book
to everyone
at
Kingsland
Elementary School.

For information regarding permission, write to Scholastic, Inc., Attention: Permission Department, 557 Broadway, New York, NY 10012

Copyright © 2006 Scholastic Inc.

Scholastic and Tangerine Press and associated logos are trademarks of Scholastic Inc.

Published by Tangerine Press, an imprint of Scholastic Inc., 557 Broadway; New York, NY 10012

10 9 8 7 6 5 4 3 2 1
ISBN 978-0-439-91177-1
ISBN 0-439-91177-X

Book Design by Bill Henderson and Deena Fleming
Printed and bound in the U.S.A.

First Printing, July 2006

Bradly was waiting for his mom to come home from work.

He was in the third grade and was old enough to stay home alone after school.

At 5:30 his mom pulled in the driveway.

5:30

3

His mom was sup-
posed to buy him a
new pack of pencils
for school. He ran
outside and said,
"Hi Mom! Got my
pencils?"
  "Yes, they are in
this bag." She gave
the pencils to Bradly.

4

He was so excited he ran with them in his hands and kissed them.

5

He took out one of
the pencils and put it
in his backpack.

Mrs. Kingsland's Class
Math time

$$\begin{array}{r} x\overset{1}{0} \\ \hline 0 \end{array} \qquad \begin{array}{r} \overset{2}{x1} \\ \hline 2 \end{array} \qquad \begin{array}{r} x\overset{10}{1} \\ \hline 10 \end{array}$$

The next day when he got to school he took it out and sharpened it.

The bell rang for class to begin. He sat down and waited for math class to start. He couldn't wait to use his new pencil.

Bradly

$$2. \begin{array}{r} 2 \\ \times 8 \\ \hline 16 \end{array}$$

$$3. \begin{array}{r} 1 \\ \times 7 \\ \hline 7 \end{array}$$

$$7. \begin{array}{r} 2 \\ \times 0 \\ \hline 20 \end{array}$$

$$6. \begin{array}{r} 1 \\ \times 2 \\ \hline 2 \end{array}$$

$$4. \begin{array}{r} 1 \\ \times 12 \\ \hline 12 \end{array}$$

$$5. \begin{array}{r} 16 \\ \times 2 \\ \hline 32 \end{array}$$

$$10. \begin{array}{r} 1 \\ \times 14 \\ \hline 14 \end{array}$$

$$9. \begin{array}{r} 8 \\ \times 3 \\ \hline 24 \end{array}$$

$$12. \begin{array}{r} 2 \\ \times 13 \\ \hline 26 \end{array}$$

$$15. \begin{array}{r} 3 \end{array}$$

$$11. \begin{array}{r} 2 \\ \times 14 \\ \hline 28 \end{array}$$

$$14. \begin{array}{r} 2 \\ \times 7 \end{array}$$

The teacher gave them multiplication problems to work on. He began to multiply using his new pencil. It worked great!

8

Bradly needed to blow his nose so he set his pencil down and went up to the teacher's desk to get a tissue.

Mrs. Kingsland's class

Math time

$x\frac{1}{8}$ $x\frac{7}{1}$ $\frac{10}{2}$ $x\frac{1}{10}$

Bradly

Billy

TOm

While he was gone, something weird happened. The pencil and eraser began to talk to each other. Eddie the Eraser said, "I bet he's gonna use me next!"

Pete the Pencil replied, "I never make mistakes so he will never need you." They began to fight back and forth and lost their balance. They spun out of control and scribbled all over Bradly's paper.

They fell onto the floor and rolled under his friend's desk. Bradly came back and couldn't find his pencil. He looked around and spotted it under his friend's desk.

He asked him, "Why do you have my pencil and why did you scribble on my paper?"

"What? I don't know what you are talking about."

"Yeah, right!" said Bradly.

11

$$6 \times 3 = \qquad 8 \times 8 = \qquad 9 \times 9 =$$

$$7 \times 7 = \quad 7 \times 8 = \qquad 8 \times 3 =$$

$$9 \times 3 = \qquad 8 \times 1 = \qquad 9 \times 2 =$$

Bradly used the pencil for the rest of the day and it worked well.

The bell rang for school to be done and Bradly put his home-work and his pencil in his bag.

The pencil and eraser began to argue again. Pete the Pencil said, "I was right, he used me more today."

Eddie the Eraser replied, "He used me more because you make so many mistakes!" Eddie became angry and started to erase the answers Pete had written on Bradly's homework.

2 X 6 =

1 2 3

5 6

7

13

Pete yelled, "Stop!"
They tried to chase
each other but only
flip-flopped back
and forth and tore
a hole in Bradly's
homework.

14

Bradly got to school the next day. He opened up his bag and found his homework with no answers and torn up into pieces. His teacher asked for the homework and Bradly turned his in.

Oh no!

Later on that day, his teacher asked Bradly to come up to her desk. The teacher, Mrs. Kingsland, said, "What is this disgraceful work?" She then told him, "You better shape up, mister, or I will call your parents."

16

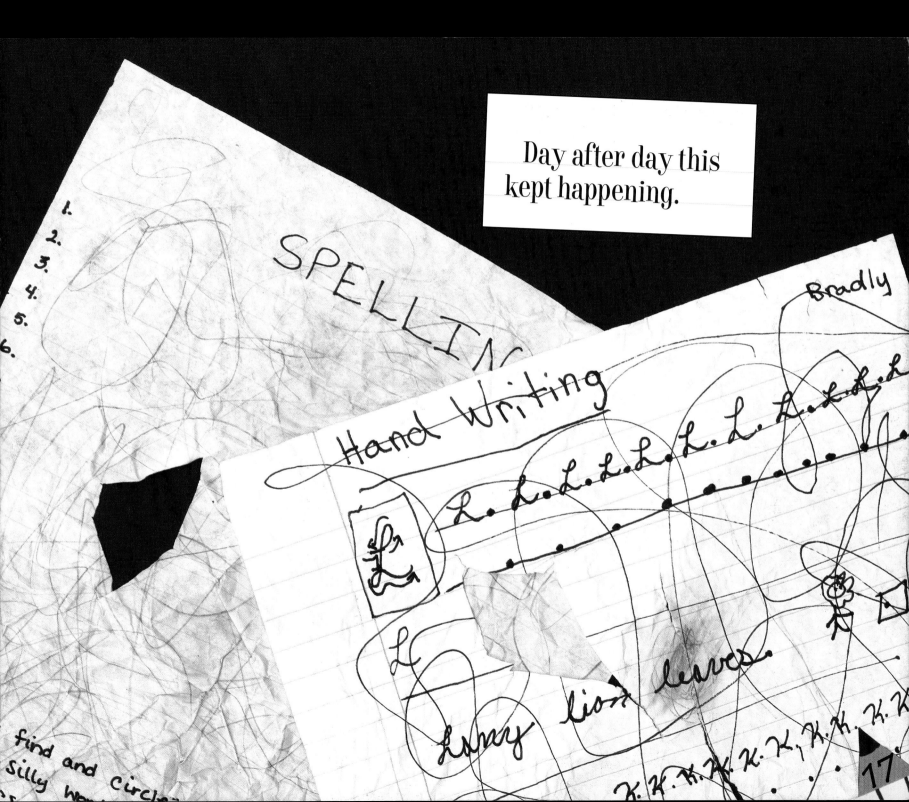

Day after day this
kept happening.

SPELLING

1.
2.
3.
4.
5.
6.

find and circle
silly

Hand Writing   Bradly

L. L. L. L. L. L. L.

L

L

long lion leaves.

K. K. K. K. K. K. K.

17

Bradly	1	2	3	4
Gym	B+			
Music	A-			
Computer	C+			Comments:
Spelling	F			2 Shape up
Math	F			Mister!!
Science	F			
Art	F			3
Social Studies	F			
Hand Writing	F			

Report card day came. Bradly looked at his report card and saw F's for everything except gym, music, and computer.

He screamed! He knew he was going to be in trouble with his parents.

Bradly	1	2	3	4
Gym	B+			
Music	A-			
Computer	C+			
Spelling	F			
Math	F			
Science	F			
Art	F			
Social Studies	F			
Hand Writing	F			

Comments:
2
Shape up
Mister!!

3

Bradly put the report card in his bag along with his pencil. Pete and Eddie saw the report card and felt bad for what they had done.

Pete said, "You did this!"

Eddie said, "I wasn't the only one!"

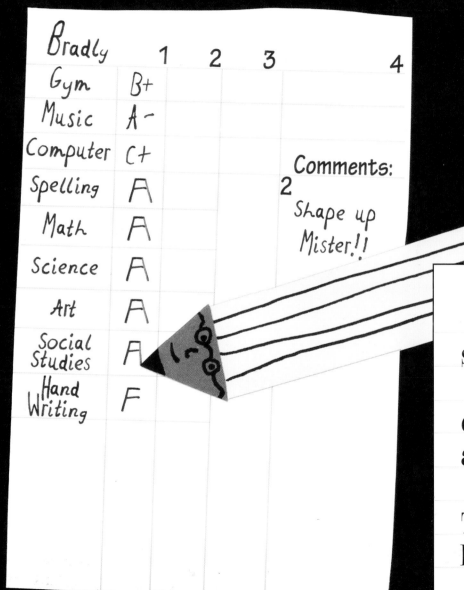

"What are we going to do?" said Pete.

"You're the pencil, just change all the F's to A's by adding a line," replied Eddie.

Pete changed the grades. They thought they would fool Bradly's parents.

Bradly got home from school. He was scared for when his parents came home from work. His parents knew it was report card day and asked for it. He gave it to them.

His mom thought he would get all A's. She fainted when she saw his report card.

23

His dad said, "How dare you get such bad grades and try to trick us? We can tell you changed these grades from F's to A's."

"What?" said Bradly. "I didn't change them."

"Now you are lying to us! Get upstairs and do your homework. You are grounded! No video games or cheesy puffs!"

Bradly went up to his room. He sat at his desk and said, "Why can't I get good grades? I put down the right answers and try my hardest, but something weird keeps happening to my papers."

He picked up his pencil and said, "I give up!"
He bent his pencil and almost broke it.

Just then Bradly's mom called him for supper. He set the pencil down and went downstairs.

That Was a Close One!

Pete said, "We almost got broken apart because we couldn't get along and look what we have done to poor Bradly."

Eddie said, "I'm sorry I teased you about Bradly using me more. He uses both of us every day."

Pete said, "I'm sorry, too. Maybe things would be better if we work together. We will let Bradly do his own work."

"When he makes a mistake, he can use me to erase it and then he can use you to write in the correct answer," said Eddie.

"Sounds like a great plan," replied Pete.

Bradly came up from supper and started to work on his homework again. He used Pete to write in the answers and Eddie to erase the mistakes. He worked on it until it was finished and done right.

30

He kept up the good work and got A's on his next report card. Pete and Eddie were so proud of Bradly.

BRADLY

A	GYM
A	MUSIC
A	SPELLING
A	MATH
A	

Pete and Eddie also learned something. It is better to get along with others than fight. They learned how to work together.

31

Meet the Authors

Kids Are Authors®
Books written by children for children

The Kids Are Authors® Competition was established in 1986 to encourage children to read and to become involved in the creative process of writing. Since then, thousands of children have written and illustrated books as participants of the Kids Are Authors® Competition. The winning books in the annual competition are published by Scholastic Inc. and are distributed by Scholastic Book Fairs throughout the United States.

For more information:
Kids Are Authors®
1080 Greenwood Blvd.
Lake Mary, FL 32746

Or visit our web site at:
www.scholastic.com/kidsareauthors

Kingsland Authors
3rd grade

Project Coordinator: Amanda Schwarck
Clockwise from top left: Kayleigh Rasmussen, Hannah Pruter, Carly Thompson, Julius Wolf, Kerstin Strosahl, Lacey Schwartz, Kayla Mulhern, Amy Welch and Trevor Schwarz

KIDS ARE AUTHORS · AWARD ·